Tall Pictures

by Raoul Welsch
illustrated by Alan Flinn

Harcourt

SCHOOL PUBLISHERS

Requests for permission to make copies of any part of the work should be addressed to School Permissions and Copyrights, Harcourt, Inc., 6277 Sea Harbor Drive, Orlando, Florida 32887-6777. Fax: 407-345-2418.

HARCOURT and the Harcourt Logo are trademarks of Harcourt, Inc., registered in the United States of America and/or other jurisdictions.

Printed in China

ISBN 10: 0-15-351444-2
ISBN 13: 978-0-15-351444-9

Ordering Options
ISBN 10: 0-15-351213-X (Grade 3 Advanced Collection)
ISBN 13: 978-0-15-351213-1 (Grade 3 Advanced Collection)
ISBN 10: 0-15-358080-1 (package of 5)
ISBN 13: 978-0-15-358080-2 (package of 5)

3 4 5 6 7 8 9 10 985 12 11 10 09 08

"What do you want to do today?" asked George.

Florence yawned and replied, "It's too hot to do anything."

"Well, it's probably cooler outside under the trees than it is cooped up in here," George answered.

"I guess," shrugged Florence, turning toward the calendar. "May 30, 1928—say, we've been here six whole months."

They walked past the orange trees that were going to make them rich. "Everybody's getting rich in California," their father had announced confidently, "so we can, too."

They weren't rich yet because growing oranges was hard, but still they hoped things would improve. Suddenly, a car rolled to a stop next to them.

"Say," said the driver, "where's Blackberry Hill?"

Florence pointed. "It's that small hill at the end of this road."

George stared at the passenger, and then he said, "I recognize you! Aren't you Tom Towers?"

The man tilted back his hat and smiled. "Well, I guess I am."

The kids gasped with amazement. Tom Towers was their favorite movie star!

"We're filming a movie at Blackberry Hill," explained Tom. "Why don't you kids come watch? Ask your parents!" shouted Tom as they drove away.

Dad said it was all right, so they promptly raced to Blackberry Hill. A girl in a fancy dress from the 1800s leaned against a car, fanning herself with a hat. Some men in cowboy hats were drinking coffee. In the midst of it all, two men fiddled around with a black box that was elevated on a three-legged stand. George and Florence walked over to them.

"Hi, kids. Tom told me some fans might be stopping by," said a man wearing a white cap. "My name's Charles, and I'm the director."

They watched the filming for the next few days. Walter, the cameraman, showed them how the boxy camera worked. He cranked it as Charles instructed the actors what to do. Audiences wouldn't hear any words since the film was silent when it played.

"Action!" Charles shouted. "Tom, you're happy—you've just heard good news and Mabel, you're still worried, so pace around this area."

Tom smiled broadly and clapped his hands. Mabel, the girl in the fancy dress, dropped her eyes and walked slowly, looking anxious.

"Cut!" cried Charles. "That's perfect."

Walter allowed Florence to crank the camera, and Charles allowed George to call, "Action!" They were having a great time.

The next day, the crew had vanished! "Did they finish the movie?" asked George.

"I don't think so," replied Florence.

A day later, the crew was back, and George and Florence ran excitedly to meet them.

They found Walter who was struggling with a new camera. "The whole thing collapses if you don't set it up right," he sighed, "and we have enough problems without a broken camera."

"What problems?" asked Florence.

"Silent movies are finished," said Walter. "Audiences are wild for talking pictures, so all the movies are switching from silent to 'talkies.' This camera records sound onto the film." He pointed to some wires. "We attach these to microphones and put them near the actors to capture the sound when they talk."

George picked up a microphone and shouted, "Hello! Hello!" in a silly voice.

"Put that down!" hissed Florence.

"Don't worry, we're not filming," said Walter.

"You can put it anywhere, and it will pick up sound?" asked George.

Walter nodded. "We hope so—it's all new to me."

Filming went poorly that day. Tom tangled his feet in the microphone wires, and Frank, another actor, kept looking at the bush that was holding a hidden mike. Some people shouted their lines, while others forgot theirs. Charles appeared to be glum.

The next day, Walter explained that they
had watched yesterday's scenes. He said the
actors were too loud or too soft, and the
microphones had picked up footsteps and
buzzing bees.

"Now we have another problem,"
continued Walter. "Mabel is sick."

Mabel was pale, with a dazed look on her
face, and up close, her fancy dress looked
slightly shabby and worn.

Charles handed Mabel a script. "Try a
few lines. We can't miss a day. We're already
behind schedule, and we have to finish
this film!"

Mabel croaked, "I can't talk."

"You can record voices anywhere there's a microphone, right?" George asked Walter.

Walter nodded. "That's right. You saw it yesterday."

George dashed back to Charles. "I have an idea! Mabel has said only a few lines so far. She has a high voice, and my sister has a high voice, too. Mabel can mouth the words, and Florence can be out of sight, reading the lines into a microphone. I bet it will look perfect."

Charles thought about it briefly, and then he went to talk to Walter.

"I don't want to embarrass myself in front of all these people!" groaned Florence.

"You won't," said George confidently. "Just read in an ordinary voice, and it will sound all right. I'd do it myself, except I don't sound much like Mabel." Even Florence had to laugh at that.

Walter said the plan sounded fine, and Charles gave Florence the script. She read it over and over. Mabel played Tom's sister, and her lines were very short and easy. Florence practiced them with George.

Mabel stood next to Tom while Florence stood by Walter and the camera. The microphone rested on a rock.

"Just use your normal voice, watch Mabel, and start talking when she starts moving her mouth," explained Walter.

They practiced until it was time for the real thing. "Quiet on the set!" shouted Charles. "Action!"

Florence listened as Tom finished his lines, and then she began to read when Mabel moved her lips. Each line was short, which made it easy to stay with Mabel.

13

"Cut!" yelled Charles. "That was great, kid!" Everyone congratulated Florence, and filming finished the next day.

A few months later, George and Florence went to see the movie. It was strange because there were only a few speaking scenes, and Tom only sang once. Then the movie went back to silence.

"I don't think the talking was that great," murmured Florence.

"I guess it's just the next big thing," replied George. "In a few months, no one will be making talking pictures."

"Right," Florence laughed. "Talking pictures—who needs them?"

Think Critically

1. What big change in movies does this story describe?

2. How is making a silent movie different from making a movie with sound?

3. What are Florence and George's opinions about talking pictures?

4. Why is Florence worried that she might embarrass herself?

5. Would you like to watch a movie being made? Why or why not?

 Social Studies

Write a Paragraph Imagine that you lived during the time that movies had no sound. What do you think the movies would have been like? Write a paragraph explaining how you would have made silent movies interesting.

School-Home Connection Ask older family members to tell you about their favorite movies from when they were your age.

Word Count: 1,047